GRADE 4

The 2005–2007 Syllabus should be read for details of requirements, especially those for scales, aural tests and sight-reading. Attention should be paid to the Special Notices on the inside front c͏ any changes.

The syllabus is obtainable the Services Department, Tl Schools of Music, 24 Port͏ United Kingdom (please ͏ (162mm × 229mm) envelop͏

C000156339

In exam centres outside the UK, information and syllabuses may be obtained from the Local Representative.

CONTENTS

Where appropriate, pieces in this volume have been checked with original source material and edited as necessary for instructional purposes. Fingering, phrasing, bowing, metronome marks and the editorial realization of ornaments (where given) are for guidance only; they are not comprehensive or obligatory.

DO NOT PHOTOCOPY © MUSIC

Alternative pieces for this grade

© 2004 by The Associated Board of the Royal Schools of Music

No part of this publication may be copied or reproduced in any form or by any means without the prior permission of the publisher.

Music origination by Andrew Jones.
Cover by Økvik Design.
Printed in England by Caligraving Ltd, Thetford, Norfolk.

Preludio

First movement from Sonata in A, Op. 5 No. 9

Edited by
Richard Jones

CORELLI

This prelude is drawn from the celebrated set of 12 solo violin sonatas that Corelli dedicated to the Electress Sophie Charlotte of Brandenburg in 1700. They became the most influential violin sonatas of the 18th century: in his *A General History of Music* of 1789 Charles Burney remarked that these were the sonatas 'on which all good schools for the violin have since been founded'. In this preludio all dynamics are editorial, with the single exception of the *piano* in the violin part of b. 20. All violin slurs are Corelli's, except those of bb. 5, 10–12, and over the last two notes of b. 13. The trills in bb. 4, 9, 19 and 23 and the rit. in b. 22 are editorial suggestions only.
Source: *Sonate a violino e violone o cimbalo*, Op. 5 (Rome, 1700)

A:2

Rondeau

from *Abdelazar*

Arranged by
Mary Cohen

PURCELL

This piece is taken from incidental music composed for the play *Abdelazar* (or *The Moor's Revenge*), written by the female playwright Aphra Behn (1640–89), and was famously used by Benjamin Britten as the theme for his orchestral work *The Young Person's Guide to the Orchestra* (1945).

Vivace

Fourth movement from Sonata in G minor, Op. 3 No. 7

A:3

Edited by
Richard Jones

A. VERACINI

This Vivace is in fact a *giga* – the Italian form of the French dance *gigue*, which, according to Quantz, an authority of the time, is 'played with a short and light bow-stroke'. This energetic piece does indeed need mostly short and well-articulated bowing, which can however be broadened occasionally, e.g. for the dotted crotchets in bb. 13–14. All dynamics – with the exception of those in bb. 12–19 of the violin part – and all staccato dots are editorial suggestions only. Some of the slurs in bb. 3, 5–12, 14, 16 and 18 have been altered by the editor.
Source: *Sonate da camera a due*, Op. 3 (Modena, 1696)

Reproduced from *Baroque Violin Pieces*, Book 2, edited by Richard Jones (Associated Board)

B:1

Aubade Provençale
in the style of Louis Couperin

KREISLER

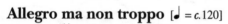

Fritz Kreisler (1875–1962) was a prodigiously talented American violinist of Austrian birth; he received no formal training beyond the age of 12 and rarely practised. As a composer, he wrote numerous pastiche pieces such as this one, which were taken by many critics to be authentic until Kreisler admitted the hoax in 1935. The dynamics in bb. 7, 10 and 43 (violin) and bb. 49 and 52 (piano) are editorial, as is the *fz* in bb. 79 and 80 (violin) and b. 77 (piano). Some ties and articulation marks have been added to the piano part by analogy with the composer's.

B:2

Hindu Song
from *Sadko*

Arranged by
Peter Kolman

RIMSKY-KORSAKOV

This piece (also known as *Song of India*) is taken from Rimsky-Korsakov's opera *Sadko,* which recounts the adventures of Sadko, a musician turned merchant who finds himself on the bottom of the sea. There he charms the Sea King with his playing.

B:3

Neapolitan Song

from *Swan Lake*, Op. 20

Arranged by
Paul de Keyser and Fanny Waterman

TCHAIKOVSKY

Allegro con bravura [♩ = c.92]

The first of Tchaikovsky's three ballets, *Swan Lake* (*Lebedinoe ozero*) was written in Moscow in 1875–6, and tells the story of a princess who is turned into a swan by an evil magician.

AB 3004

AB 3004

C:1

Drunkard's Song

No. 36 from *For Children*, Vol. 1

Arranged by
Ede Zathureczky

BARTÓK

For Children was Bartók's first big collection of folk pieces, in which he aimed to introduce young pianists to 'the simple and non-Romantic beauties of folk music'. The square-bracketed metronome marks are suggested for exam purposes. Players may omit the lower G of the chord in b. 36.

Spring Song
Homage to Stenhammar
No. 6 from *Nordic Impressions*

C:2

HAFLIDI HALLGRÍMSSON

Haflidi Hallgrímsson was born in the small town of Akureyri on the north coast of Iceland. He has composed extensively for strings, and often illustrates his pieces for children with his own quirky drawings. The square-bracketed metronome mark is suggested for exam purposes.

All enquiries for this piece apart from the exams should be addressed to G. Ricordi & Co. (London) Ltd, Bedford House, 69–79 Fulham High Street, London SW6 3JW.

Binks' Waltz

Arranged by
D. Fraser

JOPLIN

D.S. al Fine

Scott Joplin (1867/8–1917) is best known as a ragtime composer, but he also wrote in other styles. Published in 1905, for solo piano, this waltz was written for James Allen Morgens (the son of an acquaintance of Joplin's), whose nickname was 'Bing'. It seems likely, therefore, that the title should have been *Bing's Waltz* instead of *Binks' Waltz*.

Checklist of Scales and Arpeggios

Candidates and teachers may find this checklist useful in learning the requirements of the grade. Full details of the forms of the various requirements, including details of rhythms, starting notes and bowing patterns, are given in th syllabus and in the scale books published by the Board.

Grade 4

			separate bows						slurred					
Major Scales									*two beats to a bow*					
	A♭ Major	2 Octaves												
	A Major	2 Octaves												
	B♭ Major	2 Octaves												
	C Major	2 Octaves												
	D Major	2 Octaves												
Minor Scales (*melodic* or *harmonic*)									*two beats to a bow*					
	A Minor	2 Octaves												
	B Minor	2 Octaves												
	C Minor	2 Octaves												
	D Minor	2 Octaves												
Chromatic Scales									*four notes to a bow*					
	on A	1 Octave												
	on E	1 Octave												
	on B	1 Octave												
Major Arpeggios									*three notes to a bow*					
	A♭ Major	2 Octaves												
	A Major	2 Octaves												
	B♭ Major	2 Octaves												
	C Major	2 Octaves												
	D Major	2 Octaves												
Minor Arpeggios									*three notes to a bow*					
	A Minor	2 Octaves												
	B Minor	2 Octaves												
	C Minor	2 Octaves												
	D Minor	2 Octaves												
Dominant Sevenths									*four notes to a bow*					
	in D	1 Octave												
	in A	1 Octave												
	in E	1 Octave												